Teaching Astronomy Through Art Book 1

by Sharon Jeffus
Copyright 2009

I want to thank Jay Manifold
for giving myself and so many others their first look into a telescope and
an appreciation for the science of astronomy.

I also want to thank him for his science expertise.

I want to thank Elizabeth Broughton for her encouragement.

Table of Contents

The picture above shows the beauty that the sun, perched in outer space, gives planet earth. Although there are scenes of great beauty in the day, there are scenes of even more rare and greater beauty in the night.

The picture on the left shows the beauty of the night sky as seen by the Hubble Telescope. For excellent information on space go to space.com.

Introduction

Why combine art and astronomy? Some of the most beautiful things in the universe lie right before us in the night sky. To look at the sky asthetically as well as scientifically helps us foster an appreciation and wonder at the beauty of the created world we live in and an appreciation for the creator of it. To allow students to learn about it visually and kinesthetically will help them retain the knowledge about astronomy that they need to know to be able to understand the way that the ancient people used the stars for navigation, and the way scientists are planning to go there and explore their possibilites for future colonization. The saying "Tell me and I forget, Show me and I remember, Involve me and I understand" is the goal of this book; to be involved in the fascinating study of astronomy and its possibilities for the future. The goal is to reinforce basic facts about our solar system and astronomy, while teaching techniques in art. It is a supplement to a science program, providing activities to reinforce learning. This book shows students how to use chalk pastels, oil pastels, charcoal, and watercolor paints, and will help them to create their own outer space art gallery.

The heavens declare the glory of God; and the firmament sheweth His handywork.
Psalm 19:1

What is astronomy?

Plato said,
"Astronomy compels the soul to look upwards and leads us from this world to another."
Astronomy (from the Greek words astron (στρον), "star", and nomos (νόμος), "law") is the study of celestial objects (such as stars, planets, comets, and galaxies, nebulas) and phenomena that originate outside the earth's atmosphere. It is concerned with the evolution, physics, chemistry, meteorology, and motion of celestial objects, as well as the formation and development of the universe.

Astronomy is one of the oldest sciences. Astronomers of early civilizations performed methodical observations of the night sky, as we will see in this book. However, the invention of the telescope was required before astronomy was able to develop into a modern science. Historically, astronomy has included disciplines as diverse as astrometry, celestial navigation, observational astronomy, and the making of calendars, Professional astronomy is nowadays is sometimes considered the same as astrophysics. As seen below, some of the most beautiful sights ever to behold are seen in the night sky.

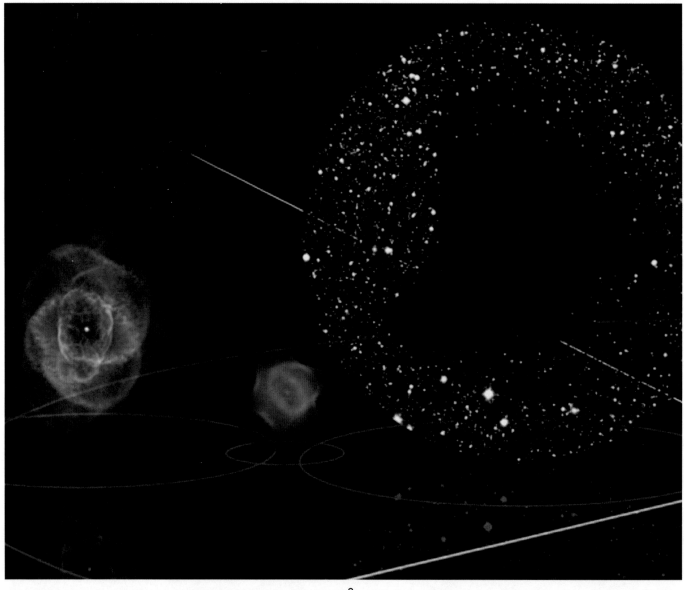

Tribute to the Astronomers

Below you see some of the few master works of art about the heroes of astronomy. From them, we can see the original primitive tools that advanced early astronomy as a science. You don't see any electric light bulbs! These men studied the stars with the intensity of any modern day scientist using primitive tools.

Johannes Vermeer - The Astronomer (1668)

Dou, Gerard - Astronomer by Candlelight - c. 1665.

Chinese astronomer 1675
Astronomy in China has a very long history, and some historians believe they were the most accurate observers of the stars anywhere in the world before the Arabs.

David Rittenhouse 1732

Creating an Outer Space Art Gallery

These space art pictures are owned by NASA. The pictures you do will be owned by you. You can go to the NASA art gallery at and enjoy outer space art:
http://www.nasa.gov/multimedia/mmgallery/index.html

We will be doing many pictures similar to the one below. Below we have a monochromatic color scheme. In art, much can be learned about mixing and blending colors and using shading, shadow and texture ot get a picture to be interesting. We will be learning how to achieve these techniques. In atmospheric perspective, the sky is always darker at the top. Go to this website for a wond3erful competition you can enter at the end of the book: http://tiny.cc/89qvX
You can even enter this competition to design a space settlement:
http://www.nas.nasa.gov/Services/Education/SpaceSettlement/Contest/

Supplies needed for the art part of this book are as follows:

1. package of black construction paper
2. package of white drawing paper
3. 2H pencils
The common #2, or HB grade pencil in the middle of the range will be adequate. Harder pencils are most often used for drafting purposes, while softer grades are usually preferred by artists. An Ebony drawing pencil is a good choice.
4. Chalk pastels or Sepia drawing sticks   Sanguine and Sienna are traditional earth pigments whose warm reddish-brown tones work well in art when used along with willow charcoal.
5. Oil pastels
You will need a set of oil pastels. Any quality will do. These can be used to color very hard and get beautiful pictures on black paper by learning how to blend these like paint.
6. Colored pencils
You will need a set of colored pencils, in particular, the light colors available, perhaps even gel pens.
7. Assorted colored paper scraps, glue, scissors.
8. Compass, protractor and ruler (websites are given on use of these tools.
9. Clay
10. Tube water colors
You can get these supplies yourself or order an art kit from Visual Manna to go with this book. Go to visualmanna.com for information.

The purpose of this book is not only teaching astronomy basics, drawing basics, but also techniques in using oil and chalk pastels. Using oil pastels on white paper first and then black paper, shows students how to make planets and outer space scenes look real. Adding stars shows depth in the picture.

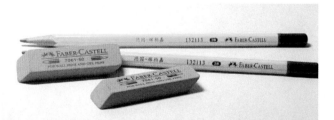

What is a telescope?

A telescope is an instrument designed for the observation of far away objects by the collection of electromagnetic radiation. Go to this website to read about electromagnetic radiation: http://en.wikipedia.org/wiki/Electromagnetic_radiation. The first known practically functioning telescopes were invented in the Netherlands at the beginning of the 17th century when in 1608 it appeared in the Netherlands. The word telescope comes from the Greek words tele = 'far' and skopein = 'to look' or 'see.' When you look through a telescope you can see far into the distance, many times farther than you can see with the natural eye. There are many different kinds of telescopes. The picture below shows you some. Notice that all of them are made of cylinders.

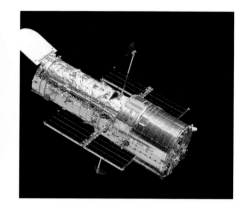
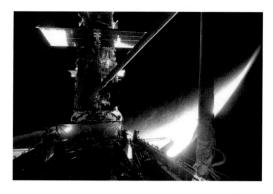

Telescopes in Outer Space

All of these pictures are of the Hubble Telescope. They are each from a different perspective and have something different in each of them. Which picture do you like of the Hubble Telescope? The Hubble Space Telescope (HST) is one of the largest and most versatile space telescopes that was carried into orbit by the space shuttle in April 1990. Write a sentence about each view of the Hubble Telescope. Make sure you say something different in each sentence. Draw your favorite picture on black paper.

After you have done the exercises on the next two pages, choose one of the telescopes on the preceeding page and draw it. Notice below you will see how to draw a cylinder. All artists have a different style. Some artists shade using smudging and some use stroking.

Shading a cylinder or a sphere.

The quickest way to make something look three dimensional is to apply, shading, shadow and texture.

The purpose of shading is to make the object dark on one side and light on the other, with the easiest gradient as possible.

LIGHT

Draw a cylinder.

Pick the direction the light is coming from.

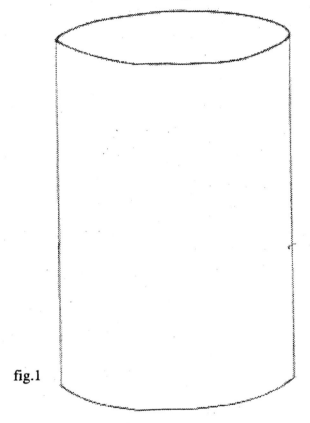

fig.1

the shade. #3 is just straight lines, the more lines the darker. #4 is contour lines. These lines follow the shape. The lines are made longest first, and then shorter and shorter lines are added between each line. #5 is shading made by a pile of pencil lead (graphite) placed on the paper and spread out with a smudge stick or forefinger.

LIGHT

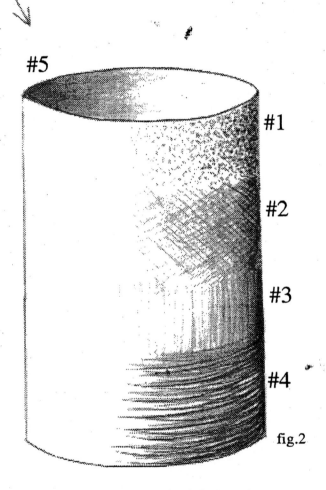

fig.2

Shade the cylinder. Try several techniques to determine which one you like best. Some techniques may work better for you on one kind of picture than another, so get familiar with all of them.

In fig.2, I used several techniques on the same cylinder. #1 is pointillism; the use of dots or points; the more dots, the darker the shading. #2 is cross hatching, the more cross hatch the darker

A large part of being an artist is being observant. Take your drawings and really look at them. Turn them upside down and look carefully. Turn them over on the back and look through the paper, by holding it up to a light. What do you see? Are all the vertical lines really vertical. Get a straight edge and lay it a long a supposed straight line, is it straight? Next time as you begin drawing, remember what you observed and make corrections before you darken your lines.

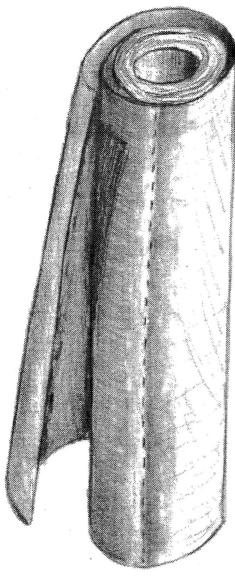

We can practice shading any cylinder before we begin to draw our telescope. A can from the kitchen is a cylinder. A roll of paper towels is a cylinder. Practice drawing some cylinders around the house before you begin.

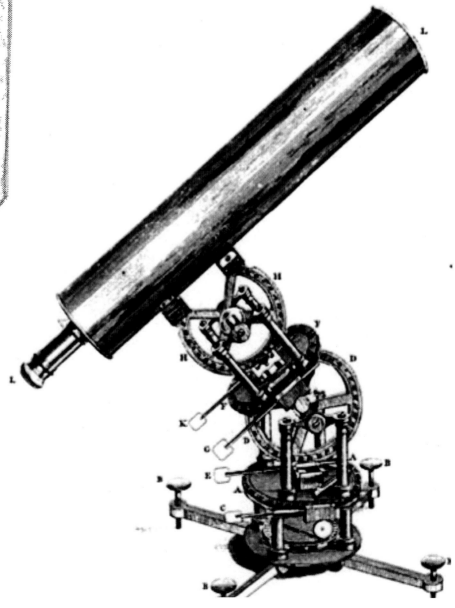

ames Short's reflecting elescope with equatorial nount from 1750 is seen on the ight.

A reflecting telescope is an ptical telescope which uses a ingle or combination of urved mirrors that reflect light nd form an image. A curved rimary mirror is the reflector elescope's basic optical lement.

How could you make omething look like a curved nirror? You could find a urved object and cover it. with luminum foil.

"'Visitors to Birr have sometimes commented on the absence of any biography of my great-grandfather and grandfather, remarking that the lack is curious in view of their contributions to scientific knowledge. I believe that two main reasons have accounted for this till the present time. First, they never kept the results of their observations to themselves; all discoveries were reported immediately to the relevant scientific publications of the day, and therefore became common knowledge. Secondly, some of their major deductions were so revolutionary that, in default of any outstanding proof, they were not generally accepted by other scientists of the time. It is only in quite recent years that the general correctness of my great-grandfather's conclusions, reached by his studies of the galaxies, has been proved. Similarly, my grandfather's estimate of the heat of the moon is now known to have been absolutely right."

These are opening words by Laurence Michael, Sixth Earl of Rosse from the forward of "The Astronomy of Birr Castle" by Patrick Moore", originally published in 1971.

Lanature1873 telescope below was built in the late 19th century.   In both of these pictures, scale is shown by putting a person in the picture. You know how large the telescope is because a person stands beside it.

Go to this website to read about space imitating art:
http://www.esa.int/esaCP/SEME8N2PGQD_index_0.html

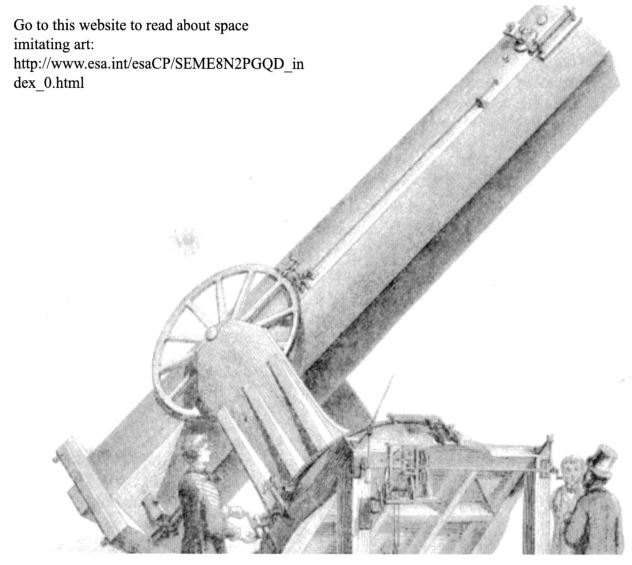

An Observatory

An observatory is a location used for observing terrestrial and/or celestial events. Here is an observatory high in the clouds. Can you draw this picture? Practice drawing the sphere below before you begin. The sphere sets atop a cylinder. Where is the light coming from? What kinds of clouds are these? Go to this website to see kinds of clouds: http://tiny.cc/Gxnde and tell what kinds of clouds you are making.

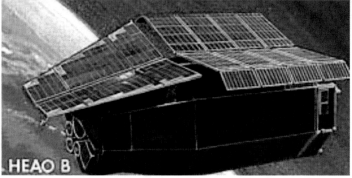
HEAO B

fig.1

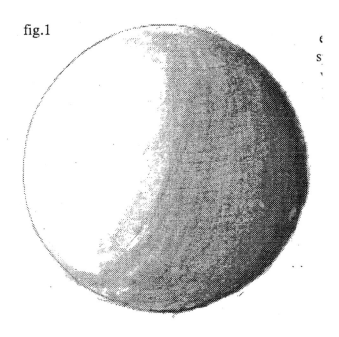

The Einstein Observatory above is an X-ray telescope originally named the HEAO B and travels in outer space. For a great website on using a compass, go to:_ http://tiny.cc/95fzB For a great website on using a protractor and other drawing tools go to:_ http://tiny.cc/EwJ34, http://tiny.cc/MAaMb

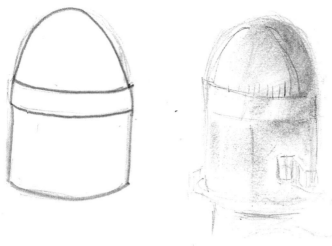

Below you see a Russian space station.

Notice how you draw the outline first, and then to make it look real, you need to add shading. The same way that you shaded the cylinder shape and the sphere shape, you shade the picture below. Never make your beginning structure lines too dark to erase. You may have to use your eraser several times before you are happy with the picture.

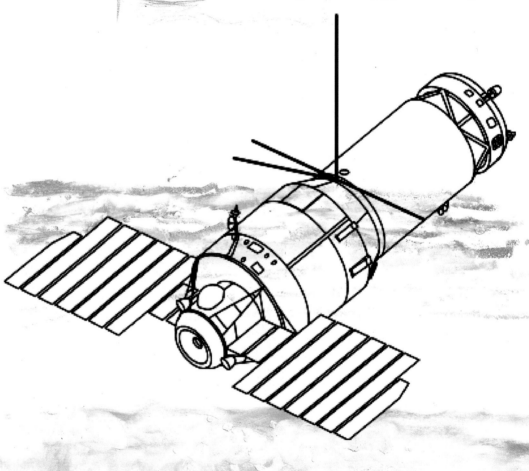

Decide where your light is coming from before you begin your shading.

All of the pictures below were made with oil pastels. Go to this website and see the colorwheel. _ http://tiny.cc/HoeCm
On the upper right you see a colorwheel that helps find direction. How do you know how to go west?

Practice making these pictures in oil pastels. Remember to color very hard. Then rub colors together with your fingers or cloth.

N

W

E

S

When you use oil pastels, you color very hard so the colors cannot be seen through and then you blend. The design above is made from the warm colors on the color wheel.

The design below is made from cool colors. Remember to rub (blend) the colors together to make them smooth.

The planet on the lower right is made from neutral colors. Notice how it is shaded.

Galileo

One of the most famous astronomers in all of history was Galileo. Galileo has been called the "father of modern observational astronomy,"

He supported heliocentrism publicly. This is the theory that the sun is the center of the solar system.

A wonderful art project is to make a telescope from a paper towel roll. Have yarn, glue, (cotton for beard), colored paper, etc ready to put on your roll. You want to make it look like a stand up Galileo. Remember that something you can go all the way around is three dimensional art. You can put a black piece of paper decorated as the solar system and stars over one end,

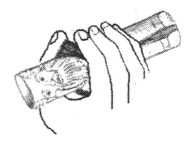

Below you see actual writing that Galileo did on his observations in astronomy. When you take your visit to a planetarium or look through a telescope, be sure and make notes on what you see.

Write an expository essay on how to make a Galileo telescope. Go to this website to read about how to do it: http://www.geocities.com/SoHo/Atrium/1

When you are drawing a face, you need to use the classic Greek proportions. First draw n oval. Go to this website for an excellent lesson on drawing a face:http://tiny.cc/0CcDv. I lways put the eyes on first. You can actually put 5 eyes across the face of someone. Always draw the nostrils first and then use shading to fill in the nose. What are some of he most prominent things about the picture of the great Galileo?

This picture done in 1872 by Jan Matejko is called Copernicus's "A Conversation with God." Copernicus was another very famous astronomer who was the first astronomer to formulate a comprehensive heliocentric cosmology theory. How many cylinder shapes do you see in the picture above? Where is the light coming from? How many tools of astronomy to you see in the picture?

Joke:

On looking through a telescope: I thought "The Martians have arrived!", but then I realised that I was looking at pollen slightly out of focus. (on looking through his telescope - quoted in the Observer, March 2003)

cosmology- This is the study of the universe as a whole and man's place in it.

Below we have a picture of Copernicus. One of the best ways to learn how to draw a face, is to cut a picture in half and draw the other half. This is a perfect size. Cut this picture in half and draw the other half. Nicolaus Copernicus (19 February 1473 – 24 May 1543) was the first astronomer to formulate a theory about the earth not being the center of the universe, thereby starting modern astronomy.

The two pictures on the right are by Vincent van Gogh. The two on the left are photographs of stars. Do your own "Starry Night."

The picture below is of an origami star. Go to this website to see how to see how to make one:

http://www.net4tv.com/voice/graphics/Origami_star.gif

From JillsArt, posted with permission

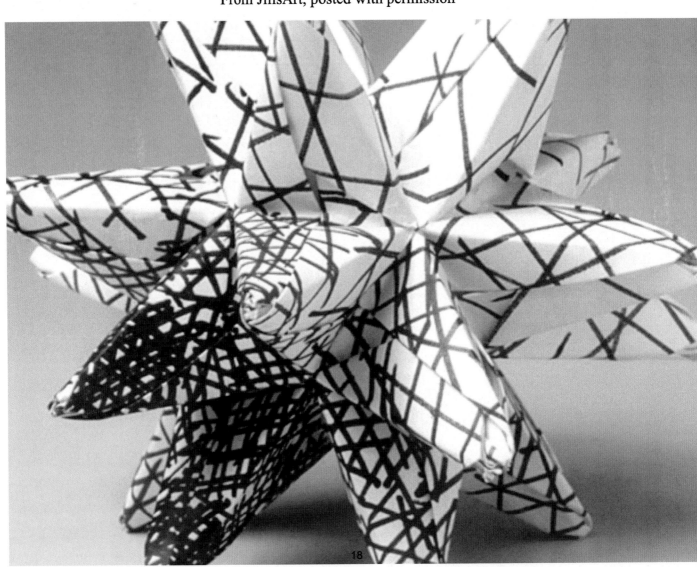

18

The Biggest Mapmaking Adventure Yet to Come

Cartography is the art of map making. If you are a cartographer, you make maps and study maps. One of the most exciting maps today is a map of outer space. The map below is by Thomas Digges and made in the 16th century. The star map on the right was created in 2008. What are the ways they are alike and what are the ways these maps are different? Go to this website to see how sailors navigate: http://tiny.cc/Vcrt7.

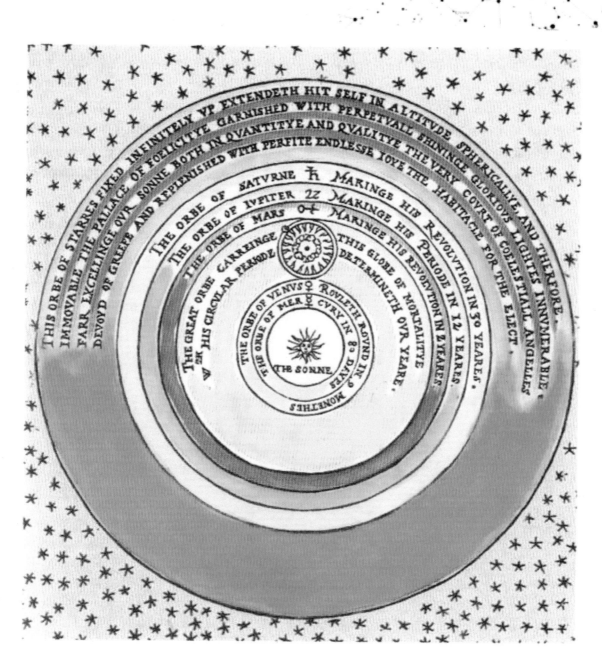

Where are we? Below left is a celestial map from the 17th century, by the Dutch cartographer Frederik de Wit. It is a true work of art. When you go into space today, astronauts map out where they are and where they are going. Do you think this is similar to when Lewis and Clark mapped the Louisiana Purchase? How can a map be made of places that we haven't ever traveled to?

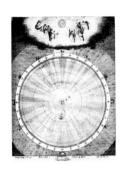

Harmony of the World, a heliocentric universe showing the planets' correct distances and the zodiacal signs with Aries beginning at the horizon and the other signs following in correct order. At the bottom are various references to Biblical passages. These are as follows:

Genesis 1:14 And God said, "Let there be lights in the firmament of the heavens to separate the day from the night; and let them be for signs and for seasons and for days and years, and let them be lights in the firmament of the heavens to give light upon the earth." And it was so.

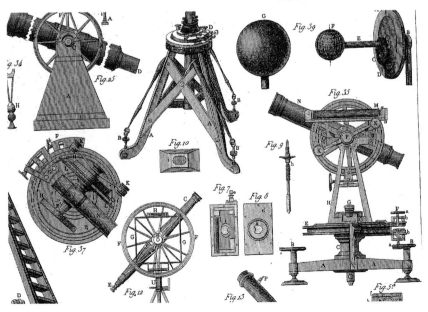

The pictures on the left are from a whole page of mapmaking and astronomy tools in the Hecks Pictorial Archive of Nature and Science from 1857. What basic shapes do you see? Where is the light coming from? Draw one of these tools and then write about what you think it did.

The picture below is done with chalk pastels. This medium is different than oil pastels, however, the shading is still the same. Color the spheres black and add white on one side. Blend until there is a smooth transition from light to dark. Put yellow under the smaller ball. Blend again. Take white chalk and make line out from the ball. Some lines need to be blended.

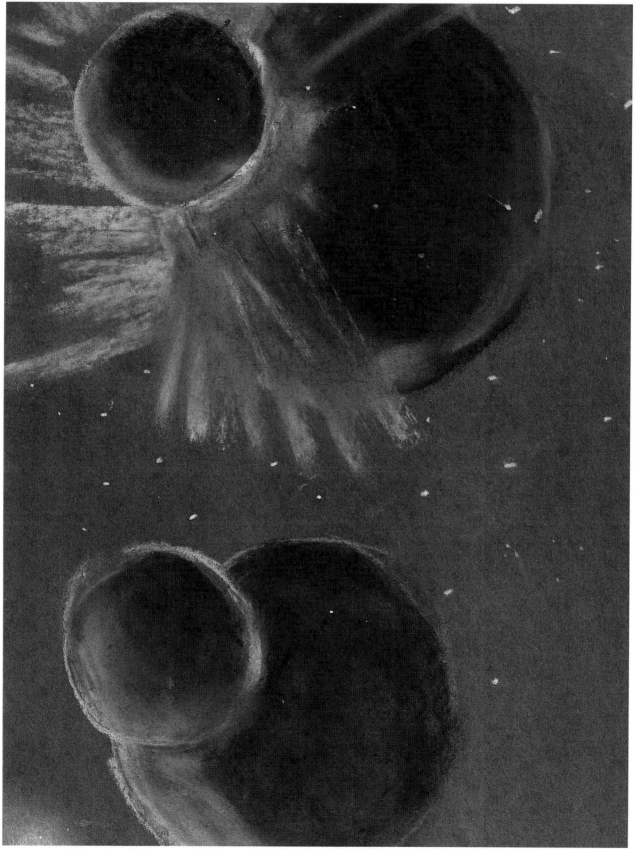

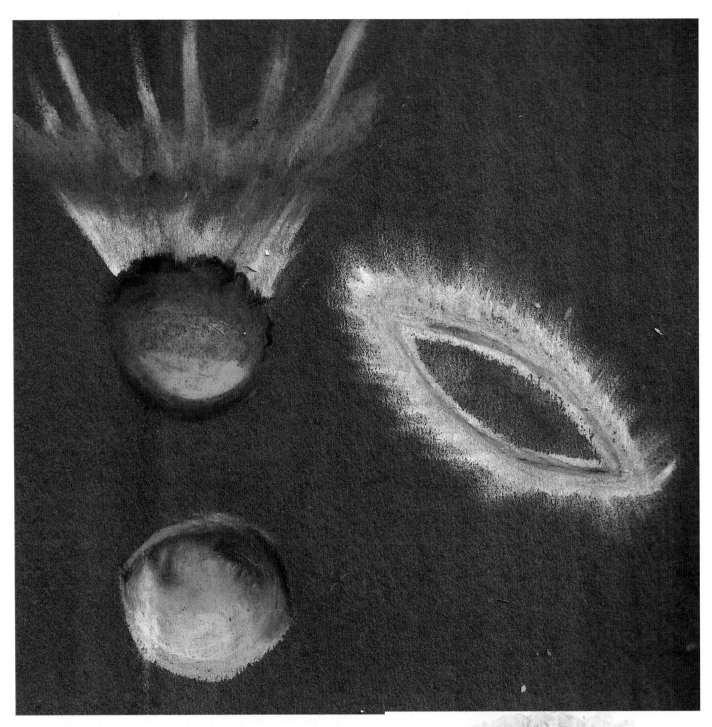

What would make the picture perfect above is many little stars around the planets. It would give depth to the picture. The picture on the right is the same thing as the planet closest above, except the one is on black paper and the one is on light paper. The light is also coming from a different direction.

When you take your white oil pastel and pull the color out, you create what looks like light coming out. Color your sphere one color, put black oil pastel on one side and white on the other and then blend.

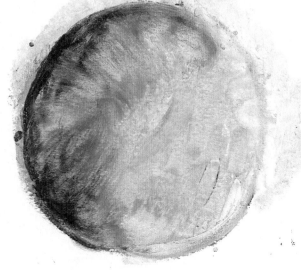

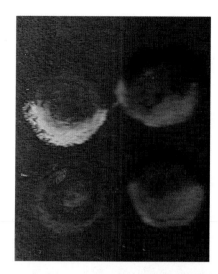

In the picture on the left, you can see the process of doing a planet. You color a circle darkly with oil pastels. You add white on one side and black on the other. You blend. You add details to give depth. Abby Miller, age 13, did the picture below. She put her oil pastel colors of white and purple, blended them and then took a blending stick and pulled the color out from the center. Thanks Abby, for doing such an interesting picture.

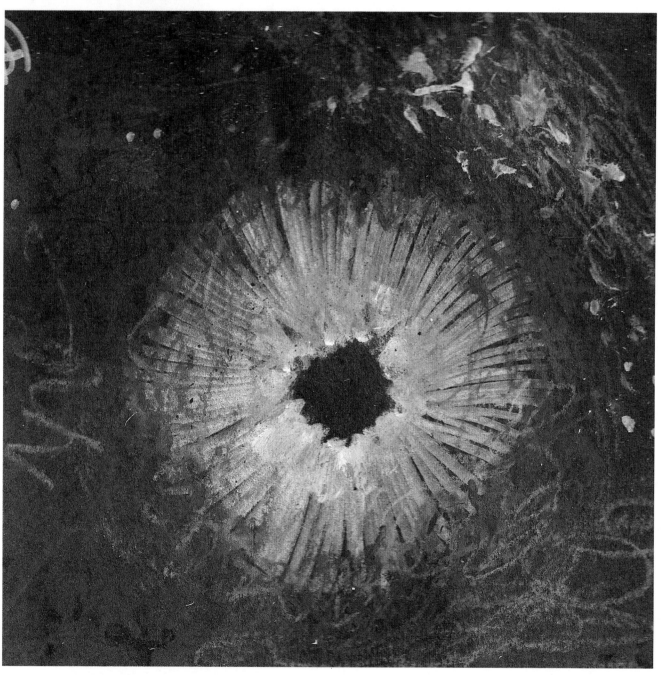

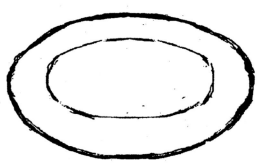

Contrast

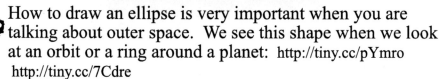

How to draw an ellipse is very important when you are talking about outer space. We see this shape when we look at an orbit or a ring around a planet: http://tiny.cc/pYmro http://tiny.cc/7Cdre

Contrast is something that is very important in art. The dark and light values come together and you have contrast. If a white polar bear is in a snow storm, there is no contrast. If a black polar bear is in a snow storm, there is contrast. Do you see the contrast in the above pictures? The picture below is done by the great master artist Rembrandt. Do you see the contrast? All the picture is like night, and it looks as though Rembrant shines a light on the man and only paints what is light. In outer space art, that is what you need to do.

Where in the World are We?

The picture below is of the "Blue Marble" or "Blue Planet." This is one of the most widely utilized photos in all of history. A good art project is to use black paper and use blue, brown and green oil pastels and put the land and water masses of earth on the picture. When you are done, take white tempera paint and cotton balls and paint the clouds. You will have a beautiful picture of earth. Now draw a spaceship orbiting around it.

The Moon

The moon is earth's only natural satellite and the fifth largest satellite in the solar system. The average centre-to-centre distance from the earth to the moon is 384,403 km, about thirty times the diameter of the Earth. Use a compass and draw the picture below of the layers of the moon. Label it.

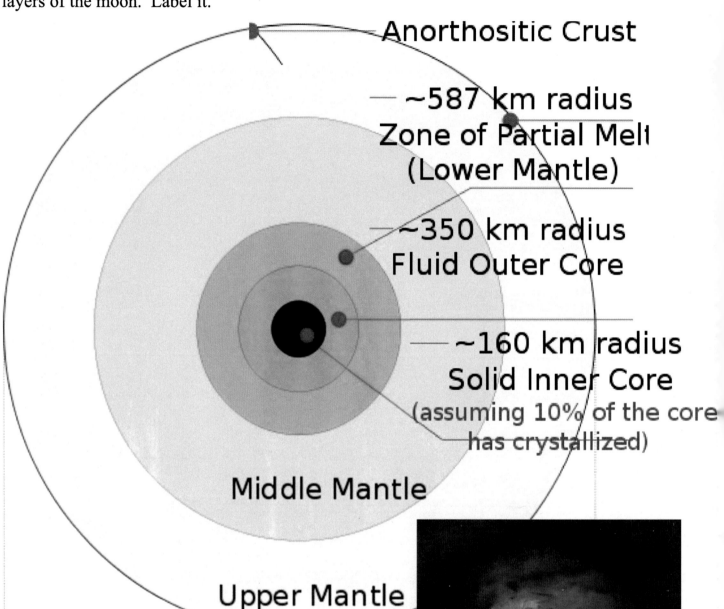

Anorthositic Crust

~587 km radius
Zone of Partial Melt
(Lower Mantle)

~350 km radius
Fluid Outer Core

~160 km radius
Solid Inner Core
(assuming 10% of the core
has crystallized)

Middle Mantle

Upper Mantle

One the right you see a man in the moon. This moon was made out of terra cotta clay with a slight indention in the areas where there is a nose and mouth. It is three dimensional art. Sculpture is something that you can go all the way around.

Mare Imbrium and Copernicus Crater are seen close up on the map on the left. Go outside at a full moon and make your own moon map. Recognize the craters and name them. You can call yourself an outer space cartographer.

Here is a picture of astronaut Buzz Aldrin on the moon. Look at the craters all around him. Below is an enlargement of the moon's surface.

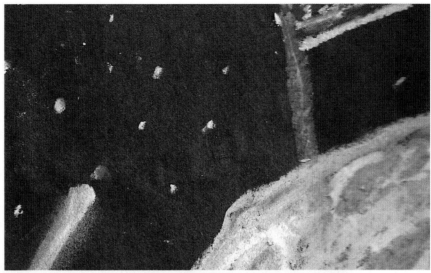

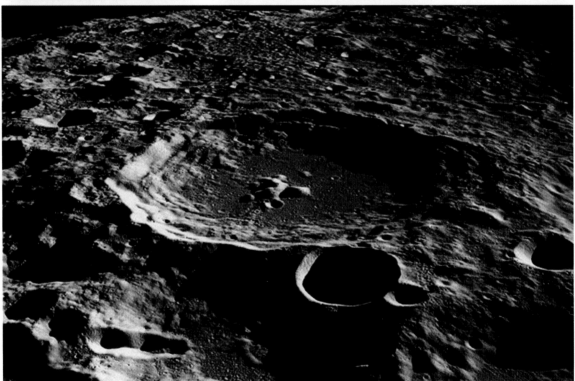

You can make what looks like moon craters by coloring one side of a hole shape one color. Where do you see the light in the picture above? Do a picture of the moon with an American flag on it.

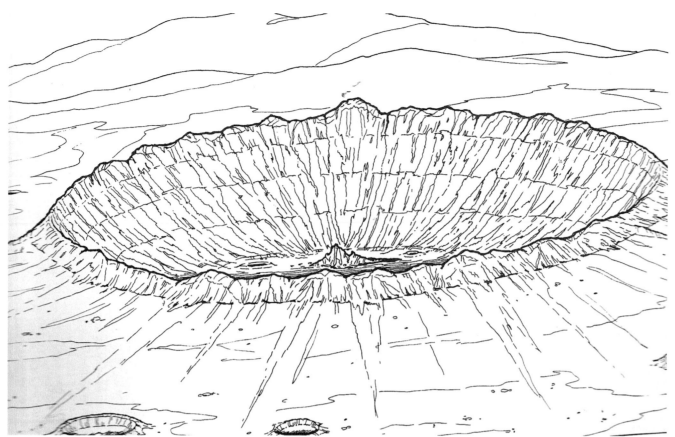

In the picture above, we have a moon crater that is made just using lines. Do you see the hills in the background? You can draw using lines, or dots. When you draw and shade using dots, it is called stippling. The moon on the lower left was done using stippling, as was the scientific illustration below left. Use a white or silver gel pen on black paper and do a picture using stippling of a scene from outer space. Do the same scene on black paper just using lines. Which style do you prefer?

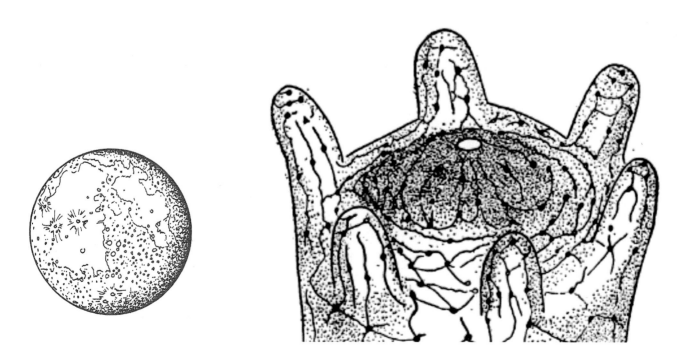

One of my very favorite subjects to teach is how to make clouds. In atmospheric perspective things are always darker at the top and get lighter as they go down to the bottom. Even the clouds get smaller as they go into the distance. This is a very beautiful picture of earth's atmosphere. Notice the many different shades, tints, values, of the color blue. This is a very good picture to do in watercolors. Notice how there are dark and light areas in the clouds. Go to this website to see how to do a graded wash of the color blue: http://tiny.cc/j2lzL. For a wonderful free book on watercolor go to: http://tiny.cc/ESLfp

Sunrise

The picture on the right is the first picture taken of an earthrise from the moon. You have probably heard of a sunrise. Compare the picture of the earthrise from the moon on the right with this picture of a sunrise on the left. What is very different?

Do the picture on the right first on black paper and then on white paper.

Astronauts aboard the Space Shuttle Discovery recorded this rarely seen phenomenon of the full Moon partially obscured by the atmosphere of Earth. Draw yourself in a space ship beside the moon. How big would the ship be? When you put something you know the size of beside something else in a picture it shows how big the object is. Will your spaceship be large or small?

On this page you see three very different pictures of the planets in the solar system. Which one do you like the best? The one on the top shows us the hot colors seen in the sun. It also shows us a pattern in the orbits of all the planets. Do you see the sun in the one on the right? Are the planets depicted in different colors in the three pictures? Which picture do you prefer. Let's do our own picture of the solar system.

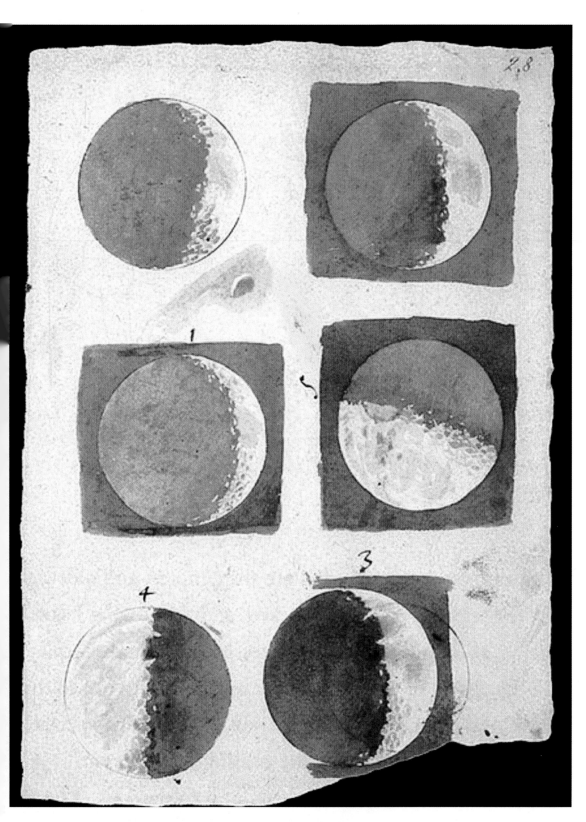

The pictures of the spheres above were done by Galileo.   When we look at planets and the earth in outer space, to make them look round, we need to think where the light is coming from.   Planets are not all the same color. As seen on the previous page, they are not all the same texture. The artist blends and mixes to get them to look real. Take a solid color ball and place it in several different positions with the light hitting it from different ways. Draw and shade at least two of them.

We read about watercolor and how to use it. We have watercolor planets on this page. They need to be cut out and pasted on black paper. You then need to flick white tempera paint on the black paper for stars. You can even use a white colored pencil, but tempera paint or a gel pen will work best. Notice how they are darker on one side.

Comets

A comet is a small solar system body that orbits the Sun.   Some people say it is a dirty snowball. When close enough to the sun, a comet exhibits a visible fuzzy "atmosphere", and sometimes a tail, both because of the effects of solar radiation upon the comet's nucleus. Comet nuclei are themselves loose collections of ice, dust and small rocky particles. The picture on the bottom right shows a comet.
Both of these can easily be achieved in art.

Gas tail

Dust tail

Dust trail

Sun.

The comet below was done by an artist using oil pastels. How could this look better? Do you think if the artist would have taken a colored pencil or gel pen and worked on the stars, the picture would have had more depth? The artist takes a white oil pastel and presses very hard on the black paper. He then wipes it hard to make a tail shape.

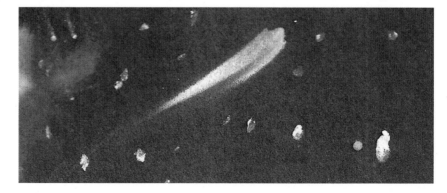

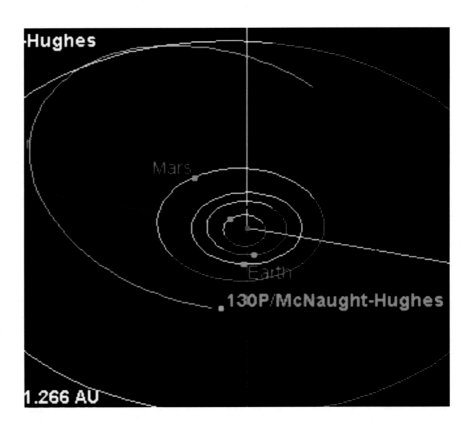

This is a picture of the Bayeaux Tapestry. It is of the famous comet that they saw in the sky around the time of the Battle of Hastings. Can you imagine if someone did a 230 foot long and 20 inch wide picture in cloth of a period of history today?

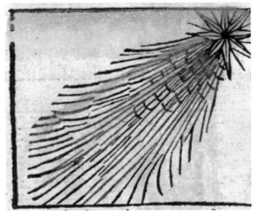

This picture created in 1493 from the :Nuremberg Chronicles is of a comet. Do you think it looks like a comet? In art, lines coming out from the center are called radial lines.

Go to this website to see a moving trajectory:
http://en.wikipedia.org/wiki/File:Incline dthrow.gif

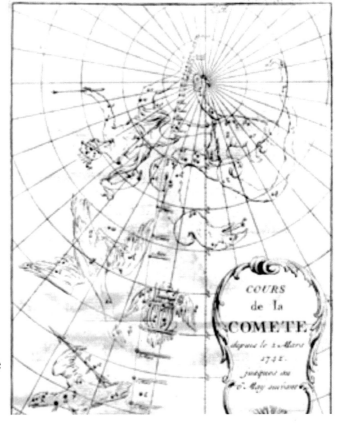

The picture above was of the comet trajectory in 1742.
The picture above it is a modern day comet trajectory. What do you notice as the biggest difference? A trajectory is the path something follows through space.

Above you see a woodcut of the great comet of 1577. There were no cameras, so an artist had to do the picture of what was seen for history. The picture below was done in the 1800's. Which comet do you think looks more real? Things in the foreground of the picture are larger. Things in the background are smaller. You can use a foam meat tray and draw a comet with your pencil, being sure to indent the design in the tray. Use black paper and paint the tray with white and make a print of your comet. Sprinkle glitter for stars on your paper.

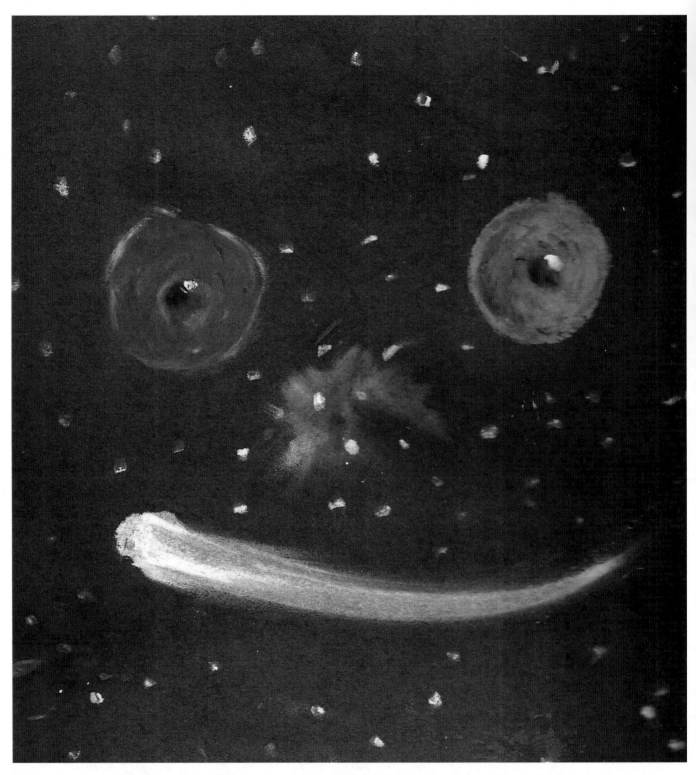

For younger children, a smiling comet is a delightful art project. The black is negative space and the light is positive space. Older students can use a white gel pen or a white colored pencil to get the stars in more detail. This gives the picture depth. Another good idea for younger children is to purchase a foam ball. You can put aluminum foil around it and then take silver streamers and poke into the ball. Children can throw the ball and watch the tail fly. They can also attach the ball to a string and run with it so they can watch the tail of the comet like a kite.

The Sun

Sunlight, in the broad sense, is the total spectrum of the electromagnetic radiation given off by the Sun. On Earth, sunlight is filtered through the atmosphere, and the solar radiation is obvious as daylight when the Sun is above the horizon. The sun has a very large place in the history of many people of the earth. Their various artwork shows its importance. The picture below by Turner is of an angel standing in the sun. This angel is done step by step, with the darkest yellow in the center. Cool colors are around the top.

The winged sun on the right is another very typical way the sun is seen in art. The sun has symmetry. It has wings that are the same on both sides. You can see this symbol in Hebrew, Egyptian, Greek and Mesopotanian culture. A good idea for a project is to make a winged sun and then put a photo of someone you know in the middle. You could also put a color wheel in the middle. You could make the wings yellow and orange.

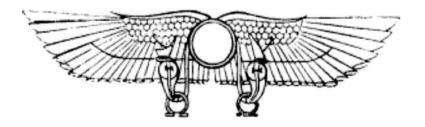

The sun symbol on the left is very common. Purple is the color opposite yellow on the color wheel. This means purple and yellow are complementary colors. Make this sun symbol and color it yellow and purple. The picture of the red sun is very common in art. There is a saying "Red sky at night, sailor's delight. Red sky in morning, sailor's warning." The beautiful picture on the lower left shows the light of the sun and its rays.

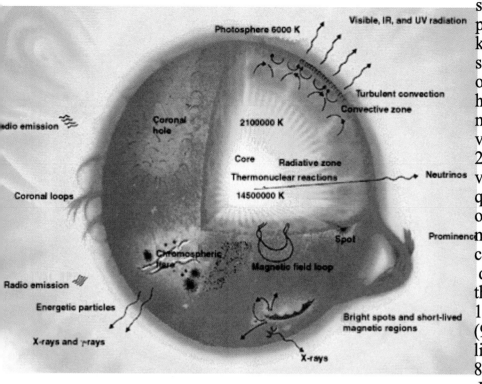

We have been looking at the sun from an artistic perspective, now we need to know a little about the science. The composition of the Sun consists of hydrogen (about 74% of its mass, or 92% of its volume), helium (about 24% of mass, 7% of volume), and trace quantities iron, nickel, oxygen, silicon, sulfur, magnesium, carbon, neon, calcium, and chromium. The distance of the Sun from the Earth is approximately 149,598,000 kilometres (92,956,000 mi), and its light travels this distance in 8 minutes and 19 seconds. It is at the center of our solar system. Can you see the core?

Go to this website for interesting information and explanations:
http://tiny.cc/XVBr4

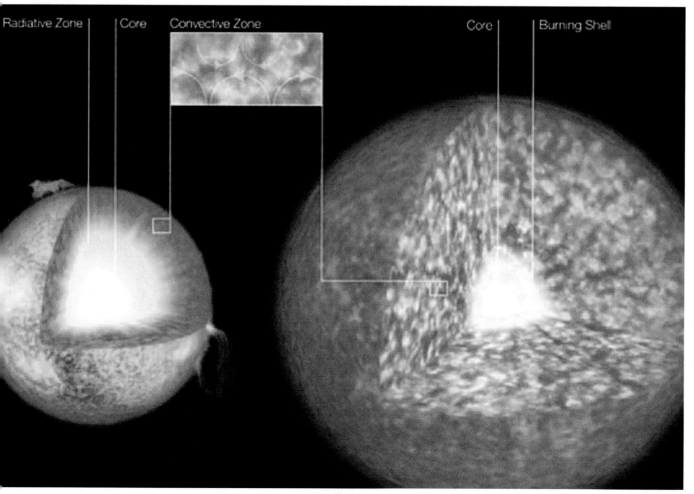

Twinkle, twinkle, little star,
How I wonder what you are!
Up above the world so high,
Like a diamond in the sky!

Stars

When we are children, this is a song that most of us know. Above we see stars
sparkling like diamonds. Below we see a young star cluster.
Go to this wonderful website to see the stars make Orion:
http://commons.wikimedia.org/wiki/File:Taurus_%26_Orion.gif
What is the difference between the picture on the top of the page and the one on the
bottom? Do you see how the black is mixed with blue on the top and red on the
bottom. Do you think it would look good mixed with purple or green or yellow?

What if you were out in the middle of the ocean at night 200 years ago?

How would you tell which way to go? You would have to look up of course! The North Star currently is Polaris because of the gradually changing orientation of the Earth's axis of rotation.

The astrolab on the upper right is an historical astronomical instrument used by classical astronomers, and navigators. Its many uses include locating and predicting the positions of the Sun, Moon, planets, and stars. It helped sailors determine local time given local latitude, surveying; and triangulation. What would they use today? Do you think an astrolab might work as well as a GPS system? Below is the flag of Alaska. You can see the North Star in its position near the big dipper. Design a star flag for a new country.

Galaxy

A galaxy is a massive system that consists of stars and stellar remnants, gas and dust, and dark matter. Typical galaxies range from dwarfs with as few as ten million stars up to giants with one trillion stars, all orbiting the galaxy's center of mass. Galaxies can contain star systems, star clusters, and various interstellar clouds. The Sun is one of the stars in the Milky Way galaxy; the Solar System includes the Earth and all the other objects that orbit the Sun. Below is the Barred spiral galaxy NGC 1300 photographed by Hubble telescope.

Take your oil pastel and draw a spiral with it. Make sure you do it very darkly. Take your finger and smudge the lines so they look fuzzy and then take your oil pastel and make dots on the spiral. Put on your stars. Remember, a galaxy is a large, gravity bound system that consists of stars and stellar remnants, an interstellar medium of gas and dust.

Nebula

The best way to do a nebula in oil pastel is to color it first with dark colors. Use your finger and blend it on the black paper. Then add your stars and you will have your nebula.

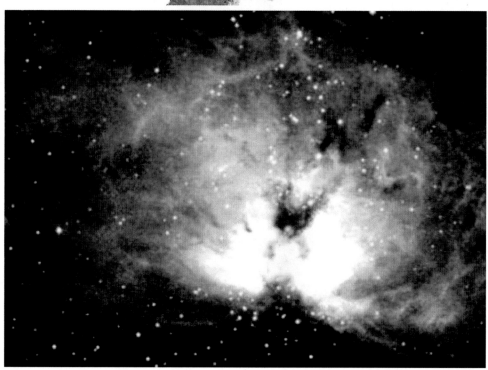

Atlas Image [or Atlas Image mosaic] obtained as part of the Two Micron All Sky Survey (2MASS), a joint project of the University of Massachusetts and the Infrared Processing and Analysis Center/California Institute of Technology, funded by the National Aeronautics and Space Administration and the National Science Foundation.

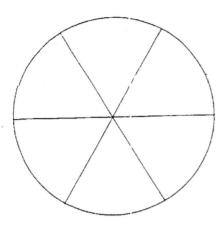

STAGE 1
Draw a circle the size you want and divide it into six using compasses set to the same radius to mark round the circumference. This method is usually more accurate than measuring angles of 60° which is the alternative. Join the opposite points to give three diameters.

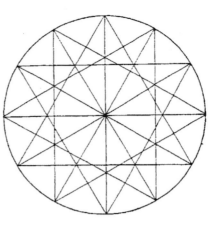

STAGE 4
Complete the triangles for the six new points as you did with the first six. The result is a twelve pointed star.

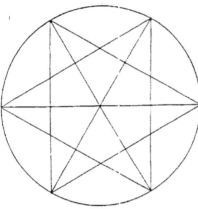

STAGE 2
Do not join each point to its neighbours but join it to the three other points. This gives a six pointed star.

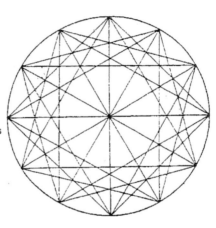

STAGE 5
Join each point to its neighbour but two to give the basic twelve point grid which is the starting point for many good Kaleidometric designs.

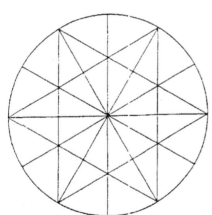

STAGE 3
Draw an additional line through each of the intersections to divide the circumference into twelve equal parts.

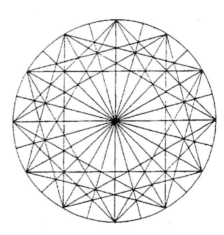

STAGE 6
Draw six more lines through the centre and the points of intersection to divide the circle into 24 points.

With its centre filled in with more 12 pointed stars as on pages 6 and 8 it is known as the 12/24 basic grid and is one of the most useful and fertile grids so far discovered.

The picture above shows you how to draw a star.
Go to this website to see another great way:
http://tiny.cc/nORKL

You can color this star above in with silver and white and yellow. How can you make it look like a star? You can stop at stage 2 or stage 3.

Sun Rays

Crepuscular (sun) rays in the atmosphere are rays of sunlight that appear to radiate from a single point in the sky. They stream through gaps in clouds or between objects.
They are columns of sunlit air separated by dark cloud regions.

The pictures on this page were taken by Jay Manifold. You can see the beautiful rays of the sun. When you do a picture in watercolor, you can get the effect of rays by pulling down the color. For an excellent lesson on painting go to: _
http://tiny.cc/S9TNF

Asteroids

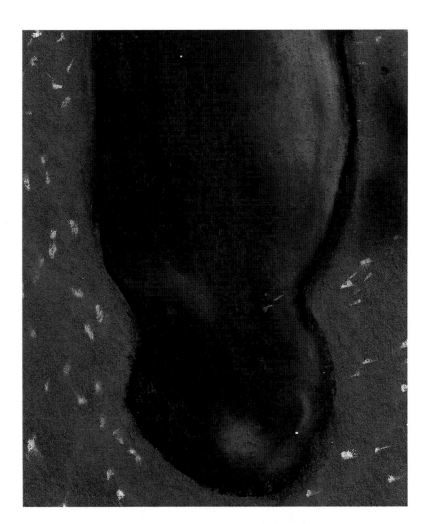

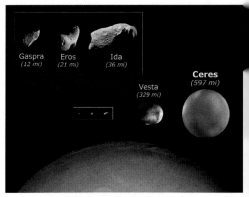

Asteroids, sometimes called minor planets or planetoids, are small Solar System bodies in orbit around the Sun, especially in the inner Solar System; they are smaller than planets but larger than meteoroids.

The asteroid above is done in chalk pastel.

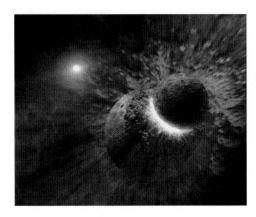

Here is a direct quote from NASA about the picture seen at the left and at the website: http://commons.wikimedia.org/wiki/File:Ssc2005-01b.jpg

"This artist concept illustrates how a massive collision of objects, perhaps as large as the planet Pluto, smashed together to create the dust ring around the nearby star Vega. New observations from NASA's Spitzer Space Telescope indicate the collision took place within the last one million years. Astronomers think that embryonic planets smashed together, shattered into pieces, and repeatedly crashed into other fragments to create ever finer debris.

In the image, a collision is seen between massive objects that measured up to 2,000 kilometers (about 1,200 miles) in diameter. Scientists say the big collision initiated subsequent collisions that created dust particles around the star that were a few microns in size. Vega's intense light blew these fine particles to larger distances from the star, and also warmed them to emit heat radiation that can be detected by Spitzer's infrared detectors."

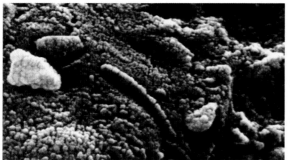

Meteorite

A meteoroid is a sand- to boulder-sized particle of debris in the Solar System. Have you ever found a meteriorite? Go to this website and read all about it: http://en.wikipedia.org/wiki/Meteorite Choose one of the pictures of a meteorite and draw it with charcoal only using shades of white, black and gray.

Drawing rocks, trees, and other natural objects are as easy as anything else. Define the space, shape add shadow and shade and then texture. Also, just like everything else, draw what you see not what you think you see.

When you learn how to do your pictures, you can use your imagination and put names or pictures in the star pictures you create.

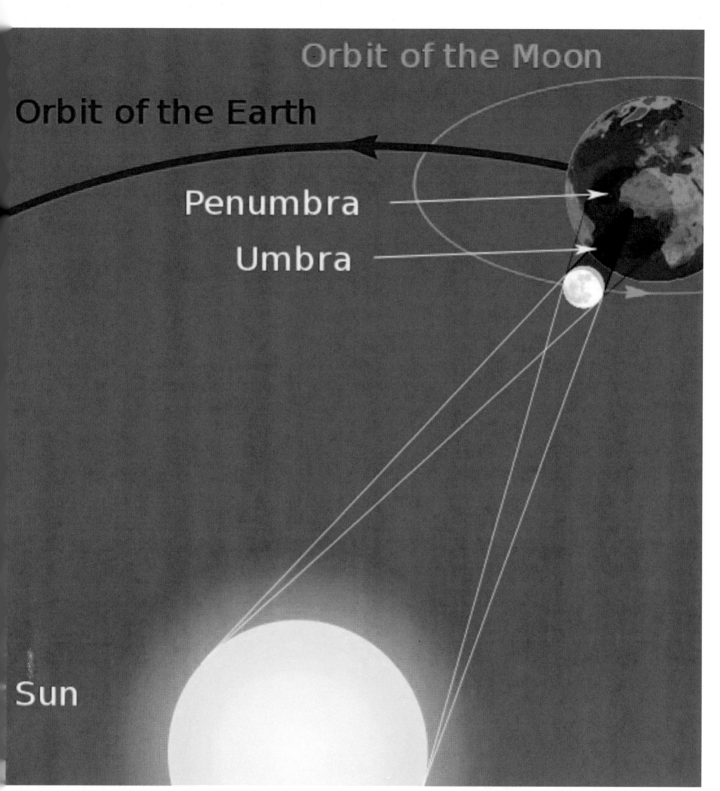

Orbit of the Moon

Orbit of the Earth

Penumbra

Umbra

Sun

Solar Eclipse

A solar eclipse occurs when the moon passes between the sun and the earth so that the sun is fully or partially covered and can only happen during a new moon. The picture above is the geometry of a total solar eclipse.

You would do the picture on the right by tracing a circle with black oil pastel and rubbing the black outward.

Negative of the 1919 solar eclipse taken from the report of Sir Arthur Eddington on the expedition to verify Einstein's prediction of the bending of light around the sun.

Lunar Eclipse

A lunar eclipse is an eclipse which occurs whenever the moon passes behind the earth so that the earth blocks the sun's rays from striking the moon and can occur only when the Sun, Earth, and Moon are aligned exactly. Some of the sun's light can be reflected, or you wouldn't see the moon at all. In the beautiful picture of the lunar eclipse below you can see atmospheric perspective in the even in the evening, the sky is lighter at the horizon line. Copy the picture below and you will learn how to do a snow picture at night. Notice that nothing is just one color.

International Space Station

Design a seal for the international space station you are going to design in Book 2.
What do you like about this seal? What might make it look international?

Inside a Space Station

What does it look like inside a space station? Can you design what a space station of the future might look like? How about the inside of a spaceship? An aeronautical engineer would design these items. How would you raise your food? How would you get exercise? Science fiction is a genre of fiction writing that is very popular. The picture below is from what is considered one of the worst science fiction films of all time. It is the 1953 film called "Robot Monster." Can you imagine a space station looking like this inside?

Outer Space Comic Strips

Good comic strip art uses exaggeration and stereotyping. Can you tell me the definition of each of these? Do you think the face in the moon is exaggerated? What can you think of that can be a comic strip character in outer space? Have you ever heard of Sponge Bob? What can you think of that could be an outer space character?

Personification is when you add human characteristics to something that is not human. The moon uses personification. If you put eyes, nose and mouth on a planet, you would have the same thing. Think of something we have studied in this book and make it into a comic character. The picture on the left is from the science fiction silent film "A Trip to the Moon." The moon is hit in the eye with the spaceship.

One of the many legends that come from outer space, and the moon in particular is the story of the Wolfman. There are many folk stories including the medieval superstition that the rays of the moon could turn a man into a wolf. In 1941 a movie called "The Wolfman" was produced by Universal Pictures. If you were going to make a man from Mars, what would you call him? How about Marsmellow Man? Choose a planet or a moon from space. Decide what characteristics would occur when the man/woman saw the phenomenon. Create a character that is effected by this. Write a character sketch about the character. You can use your Teaching English through Art book or go to this website to find out how to write a character sketch: http://tiny.cc/W3y07
Draw a picture of the person before and after he saw the phenomenon in outer space.

H. G. Wells was a very important voice in the science fiction movement. <u>The Time Machine</u> and <u>War</u> <u>of</u> <u>the</u> <u>Worlds</u> are both classics of literature. He made up a whole race of lunar inhabitants called Selenites in his novel <u>The First Men in the Moon</u>.
If you could imagine men that lived in the moon, what would they look like? What would they eat? How would the live? Write a description of a creature you found on the moon. Draw a picture of what he would look like.

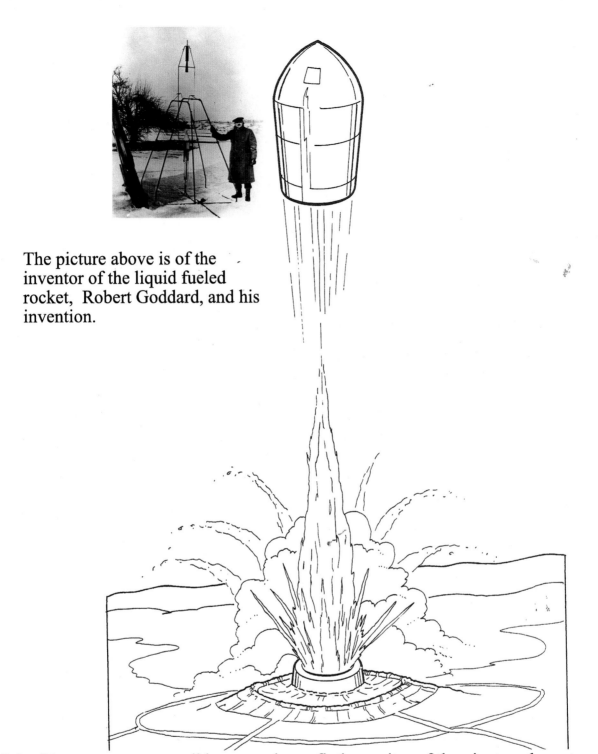

The picture above is of the inventor of the liquid fueled rocket, Robert Goddard, and his invention.

Jules Verne was a very well known science fiction writer of the nineteenth century who wrote about thrilling adventures usually involving machines of the future. He wrote about great airships. He wrote about a submarine called "The Nautilus." He successfully calculated the speed necessary for a spacecraft to go to leave earth's gravity; 12,000 yards per second. The picture above is how, in his novel <u>From the Earth to the Moon</u>, the men devised an explosion to propel the rocket to outer space. Color this picture in the brightest colors you can imagine. Color the explosion in hot colors; red, orange and yellow, and color the rocket in cool colors; green, blue and violet. Use your imagination and design a machine that any family could use for space travel. Write a paragraph on how it works.

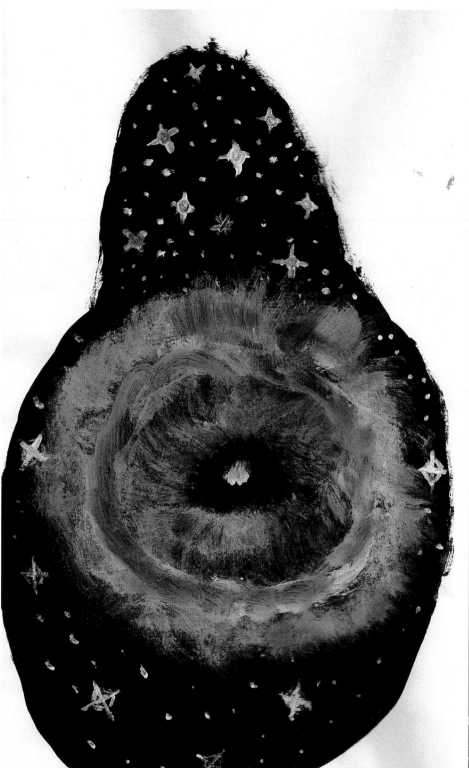

Elizabeth
Age 16

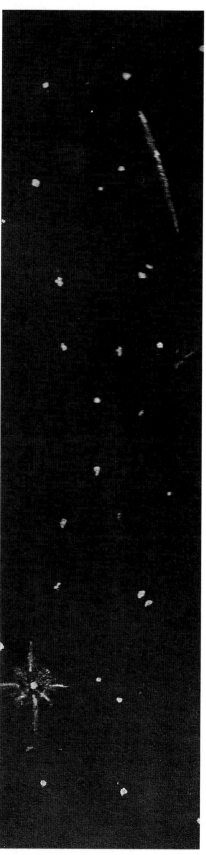

Can you guess what this picture is about?

This book is a supplement to a science book about astronomy. We recommend
Dr. Jay Wile's science books for your core science.

Contact *visualmanna@gmail.com* if you are interested in our Intern program. Students learn
how to teach art, do murals for ministry, prepare an excellent portfolio, and much more. Go to
visualmanna.com for information.

Free art lessons are available at **OurHomeschoolForum.com** and books are available at
Rainbow Resource Center (**www.rainbowresource.com**). Try all our "Art Through the Core"
series and other books as well! Make learning fun for kids!!! Sharon Jeffus teaches Art
Intensives in person for the Landry Academy at **landryacademy.com**.

VISUAL | MANNA

Educating with art since 1992!

MORE BOOKS FROM VISUAL MANNA

Art Through the Core series...

Teaching American History Through Art
Teaching Astronomy Through Art
Teaching English Through Art
Teaching History Through Art
Teaching Literature Through Art
Teaching Math Through Art
Teaching Science Through Art
Teaching Social Studies Through Art

Other Books...

Art Adventures in Narnia
Art Basics for Children
Bible Arts & Crafts
Christian Holiday Arts & Crafts
Dragons, Dinosaurs, Castles and Knights
Drawing, Painting and Sculpting Horses
Expanding Your Horizons Through Words
Indians In Art
Master Drawing
Preschool & Early Elementary Art Basics
Preschool Bible Lessons
Visual Manna 1: Complete Art Curriculum
Visual Manna 2: Advanced Techniques

Made in the USA
Coppell, TX
25 July 2022